ZAAHIR & JAMEL THE CAMEL

BELIEVE IN ALLAH

by
Amatullah Al Marwani

Goodword**kidz**

Helping you build a family of faith

2

Zaahir & Jamel are friends fast and true.
Where one goes, the other goes, too.

With a brand-new adventure each and every day,
They invite you to join their fun along the way.

What do you know about believing in only One God?
"Come learn with us," beckon your pals with a nod…

3

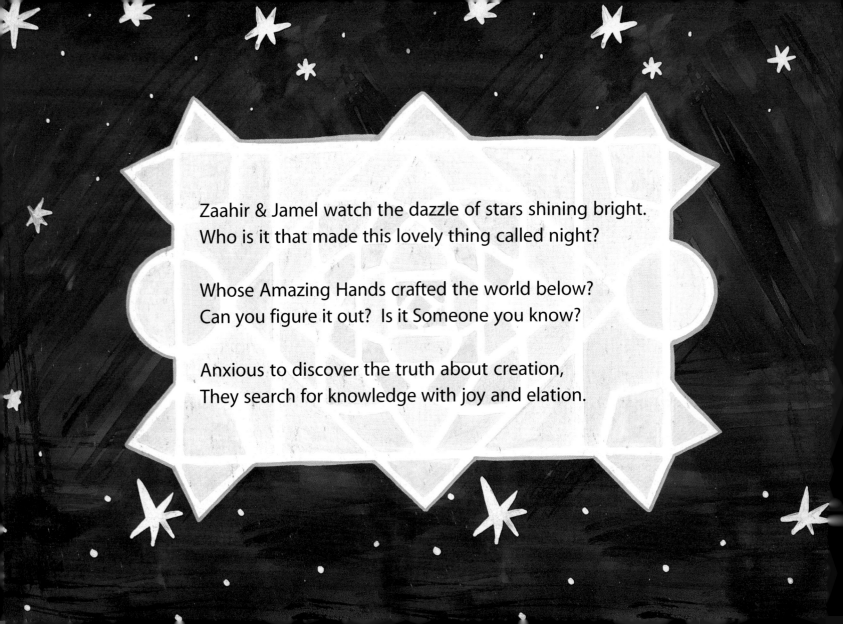

Zaahir & Jamel watch the dazzle of stars shining bright.
Who is it that made this lovely thing called night?

Whose Amazing Hands crafted the world below?
Can you figure it out? Is it Someone you know?

Anxious to discover the truth about creation,
They search for knowledge with joy and elation.

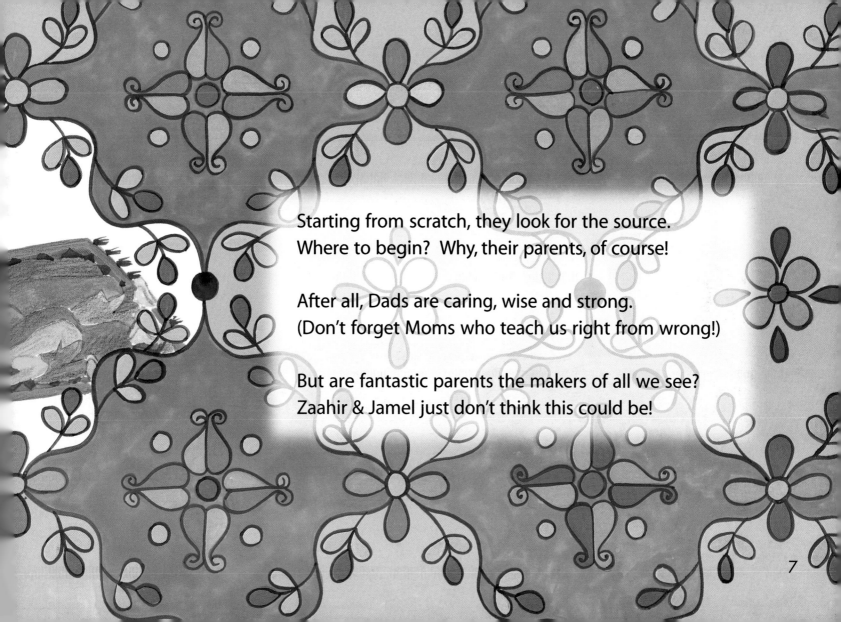

Starting from scratch, they look for the source.
Where to begin? Why, their parents, of course!

After all, Dads are caring, wise and strong.
(Don't forget Moms who teach us right from wrong!)

But are fantastic parents the makers of all we see?
Zaahir & Jamel just don't think this could be!

If not our parents, then who's next on the list?
Who created perfection with nothing lost or missed?

Zaahir & Jamel hatch out a plan.
They'll ask their teacher; he's a smart man.

Writing down everything they want to know,
With questions in hand, off they go.

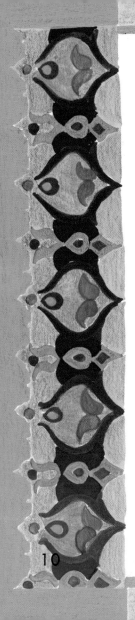

"Mr. Zaro! Mr. Zaro!" Zaahir & Jamel call out.
Their teacher stops to discover what the fuss is about.

"We want to know Who made this and that and the other!"
"We want to know Who made our mom, dad, sister and brother!"

"Whoa, now, hold on!" laughs Mr. Zaro with a grin.
"That's an awful lot of wondering for such young men."

"Okay, kids. Grab a seat and pay close attention.
There are important basics we have to mention…"

His words flow smooth and gentle like a river.
"Let's start with the Name of The Ultimate Giver."

"Is it…Allah?" reply Zaahir & Jamel, faces beaming with pleasure.
"Yes! Believing in Him is the key to Heaven, an endless treasure!"

SHOW RESPECT

Eid Al-Adha

Months of the Year

1 Muharram	7 Rajab
2 Safar	8 Shaban
3 Rabiul Awwal	9 Ramadhan
4 Rabiul Akhir	10 Shawwal
5 Jumada Awwal	11 Dhul Qa'dah
6 Jumadal Akhir	12 Dhul Hijjah

AT THE MOSQUE · READY FOR RAMDAN · HOW TO HAJJ · CHARITY CHEER

11

Masha'Allah! A Treasure! Wow! This was getting exciting!
On the edge of their seats, their finger-nails they were biting…

"You see," continues Mr. Zaro, his eyes flashing a twinkle,
"The path to our Lord is straight without even one wrinkle!"

"It was revealed to the Prophet Muhammad in the Glorious Qur'an—
ALLAH Alone is the Creator, not any other god or man."

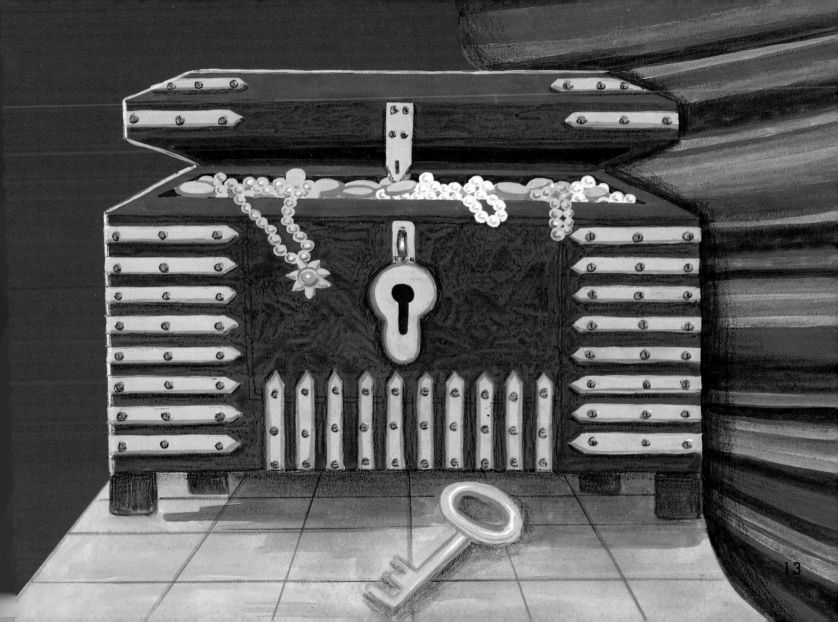

13

14

Zaahir & Jamel felt the answer was close at hand.
Everything made sense; they were starting to understand.

"Allah means 'Only One God', no partners, no help, no aide.
He is The Merciful King who must always be obeyed."

Pausing to reflect on how to best make his case,
Mr. Zaro opens his Qur'an to a very special place.

With a finger tracing the words spread across the page,
Mr. Abdur Rahman reads aloud, his voice melodic and sage…

"Allah, You alone we worship and Your help alone we seek!"
Closing The Book he said thankfully, "All Praise to You, The Unique!"

"So you see, my dear students, that no one else but Him,
Can make the sun shine fierce or make the twilight dim."

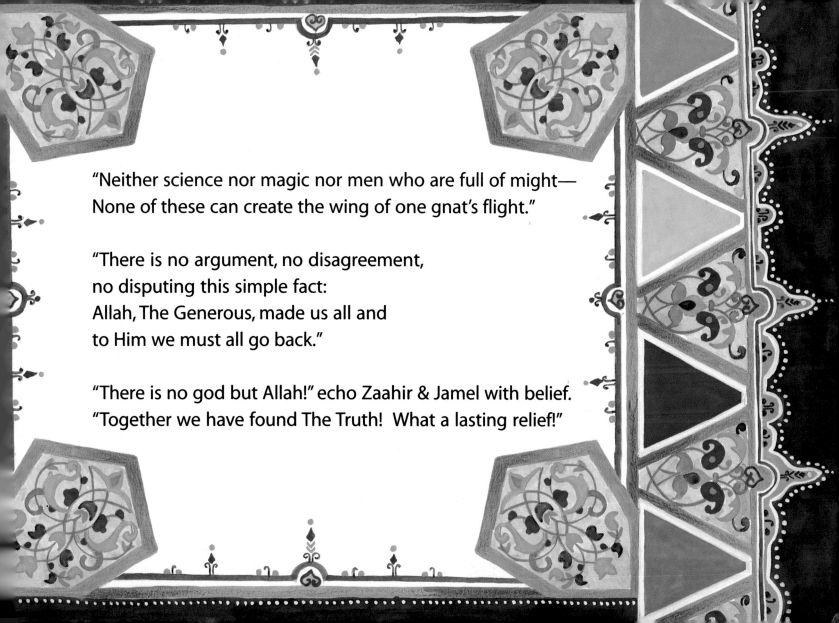

"Neither science nor magic nor men who are full of might—
None of these can create the wing of one gnat's flight."

"There is no argument, no disagreement,
no disputing this simple fact:
Allah, The Generous, made us all and
to Him we must all go back."

"There is no god but Allah!" echo Zaahir & Jamel with belief.
"Together we have found The Truth! What a lasting relief!"

Games &

Learning about Islam is fun.
Say "Bismillah" and jump right in!
You'll find all the answers on the last page (no peeking

Zaahir & Jamel's QUIZ:
1. Which surah of the Qur'an did
   Mr. Zaro read from?
   a. #1, Al-Fatiha (The Opening)
   b. #112, Al-Ihklas (Sincerity)
   c. #114, An-Naas (Humanity)
2. True or False: Believing in
   Allah is the way to Heaven.

3. Allah created:
   a. only the earth we live on
   b. only our families, flowers,
      food and fun
   c. everything

Activities

4. Fill in the blank: There is no god but _____ and Muhammad œ is the _____ of Allah.

5. Who should we ask for help and guidance?

6. How can Muslims show they believe in Allah?

Practice writing Al-Khaliq, the Creator in Arabic (remember to start from the right and go to the left!):

الخالق

الْخَالِقِ

21

Zaahir & Jamel's Quiz:

1. (A.) *Surah Al-Fatiha* or "The Opening", is recited by Muslims at least seventeen times every day during our obligatory prayers or salah. This chapter of the Qur'an has been referred to as "Umm Ul-Kitab" or "The Mother of the Book". Just like a Mom, it's full of good advice, reminders and love!

2. TRUE! Muslims work to earn Heaven by worshipping our Creator and doing good deeds, but the basic foundation of this is the belief in Allah, The Only God. Have you ever heard the saying, "If you don't believe it, you can't achieve it"? You can, insha'Allah, achieve the reward of Paradise if you start your journey to get there by believing in Allah.

3. (C.) Everything! Allah has made every single thing…things we know about and things we don't. He made things we can see (like each other) and things we can't (like angels). Allah is *Al-Badi'—The Originator* (Qur'an 2:117). Allah is *Al-Bari'—The Maker* (Qur'an 59:24). Allah is *Al-Muhyi—The Giver of Life* (Qur'an 30:50). He is ALLAH, The Only God!

4. *There is no god but Allah and Muhammad ﷺ is the Messenger of Allah.* This is the *Shahadah*, the first Pillar of Islam. There is no magic or secret to Islam. Simply say these words, then follow them with your mind, body, heart and soul to be a Muslim, the one who submits and believes in Allah.

5. Muslims ask Allah for His help and guidance. It doesn't matter how big or small our needs, Allah is there for us. Prophet Muhammad ﷺ taught us that when we raise our hands to Allah in du'aa, He doesn't like for us to lower them down empty—He wants to give us what we ask for! It's important to remember, however, that sometimes the answer isn't what we expect or want, but it is always the right answer because it is from Allah!

6. There are many ways a Muslim can show they believe in Allah. The first is to follow His commands and the example of His Prophet, Muhammad ﷺ. When we are proud of our religion, we are also showing our belief in Allah. Islam is so full of goodness, honor, morals, love and truth, it wouldn't make sense to believe in anything else! What ways can *you* think of to show you believe in Allah?

GLOSSARY

Al-Badi'– One of Allah's 99 Beautiful Names meaning "The Originator"

Al-Bari'– One of Allah's 99 Beautiful Names meaning "The Maker"

Al-Muhyi – One of Allah's 99 Beautiful Names meaning "The Giver of Life"

Allah – "The Only God"; This Arabic word is used by some Arabic speaking Christians and Jews to refer to God, too!

As-Salaamu Alaikum – Peace be with you

Du'aa – Supplication, a special prayer between the believer and Allah. You can make du'aa in any language but it is nice to try to learn them in Arabic, the language of the Qur'an. Here's an easy one: "Rabbi, zidni 'ilma" which means, "My Lord, increase me in knowledge". Ameen!

Jennah – Heaven, Paradise.

Prophet Muhammed – The last and final Messenger of Allah; Prophet Muhammed was the best example for all mankind to follow. (Qur'an 33:21)

Qur'an – The Book of Allah's Holy Words, kept safe for all of time. The Qur'an was revealed to Prophet Muhammed over 1400 years ago by the Angel Jibree (Gabriel) and it is exactly the same now as it was then—not one word has been changed!

Worship – To perform acts of obedience, love and devotion to Allah